This book belongs to …

©Illus. Dr. Seuss 1957

_____

The
EAR
BOOK

by Al Perkins

Illustrated by

WILLIAM O'BRIAN

A Bright & Early Book

Ears

Our ears

They hear a clock.

Our ears hear water.

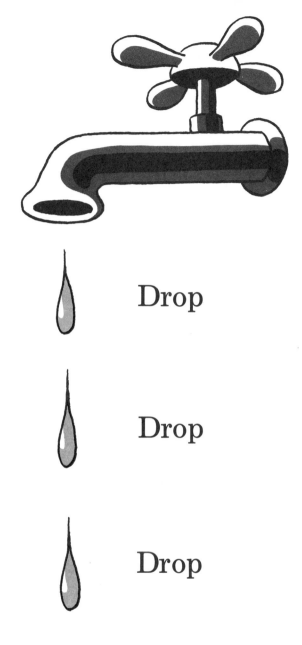

Drop

Drop

Drop

Our ears hear popcorn.

Ears Ears
Ears
Ears

It's good.
It's good
to hear with ears.

Toot
Toot
Toot

We hear a flute.

We hear a Ding.
We hear a Dong.

We hear a Ping.
We hear a Pong.

We hear my sister
sing a song.

We also hear
my father snore.

We hear my sister
slam the door.

Boom! Boom!
Boom! Boom!

Dum! Dum! Dum!

It's good
to hear
a drummer drum . . .

and sister blowing
bubble gum.

We hear hands clap

and fingers snap.

We hear feet
tap
tap tap
tap tap.

It's good.
It's good
to hear the rain.

Ears. Ears. Ears!
We like our ears.
It's very good
to hear
with ears.